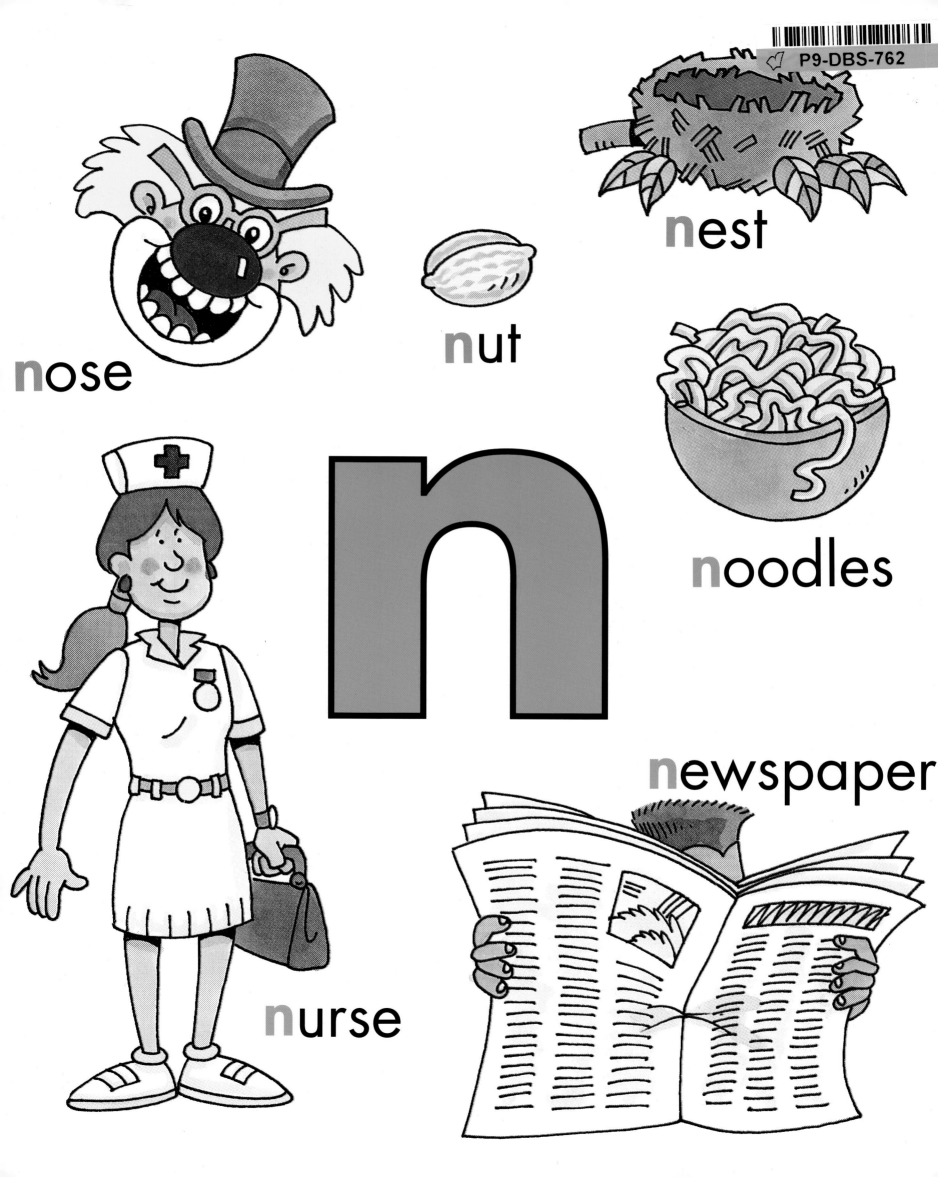

nest

nut

nose

n

noodles

newspaper

nurse

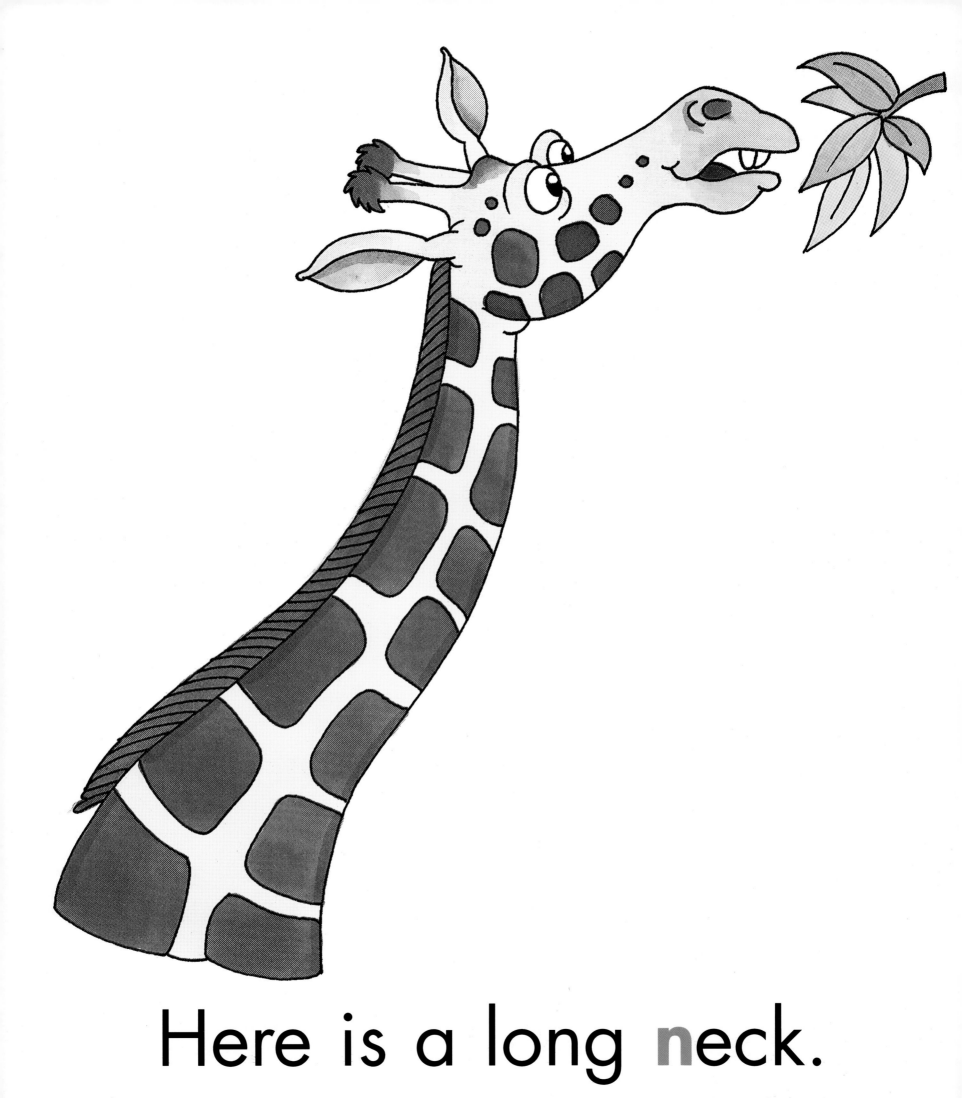

Here is a long neck.

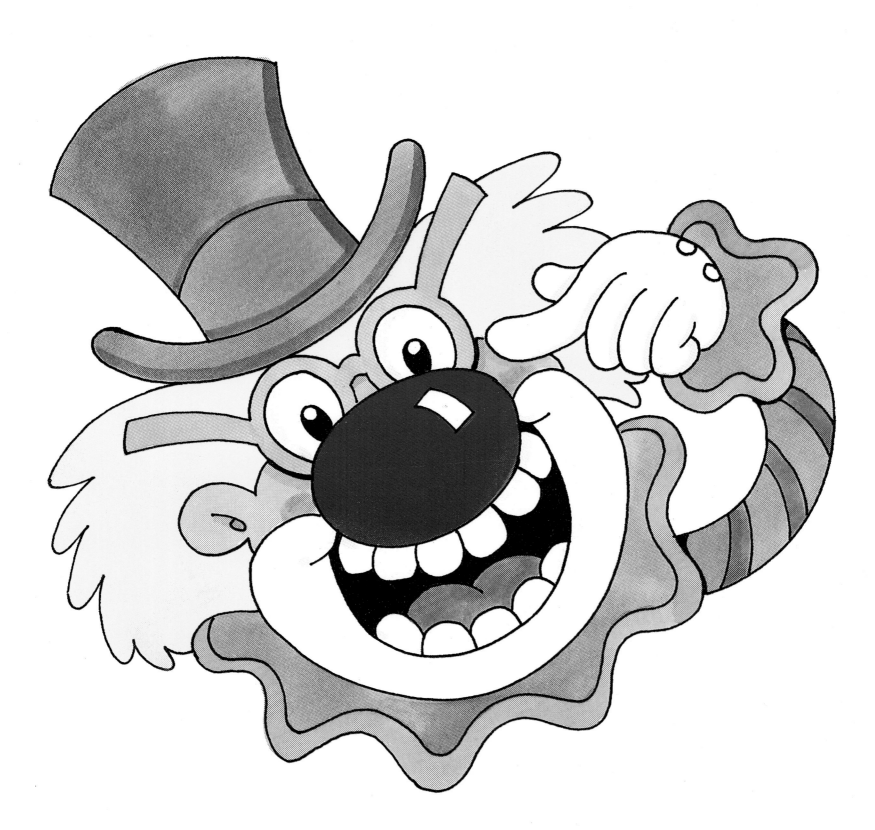

Here is a red nose!

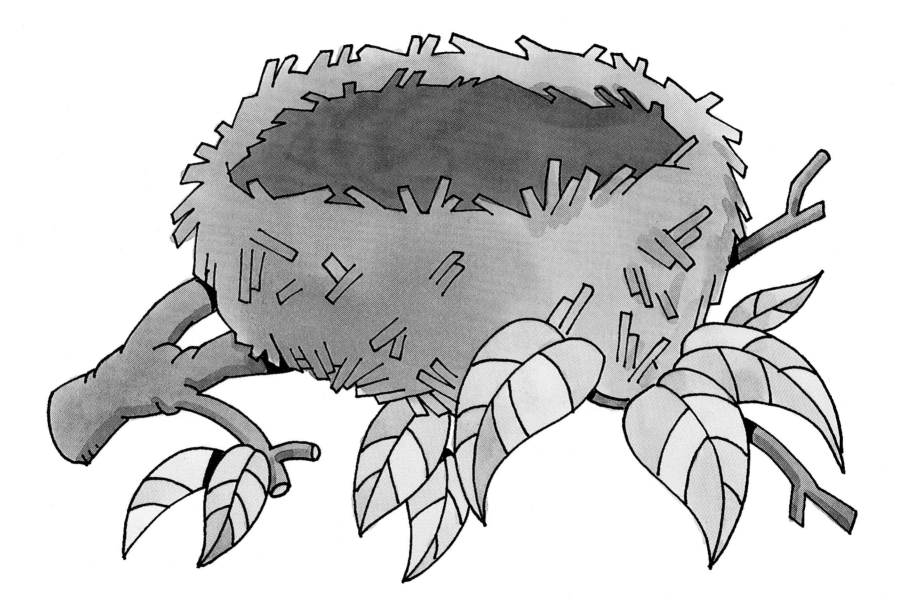

Here is a **n**est.

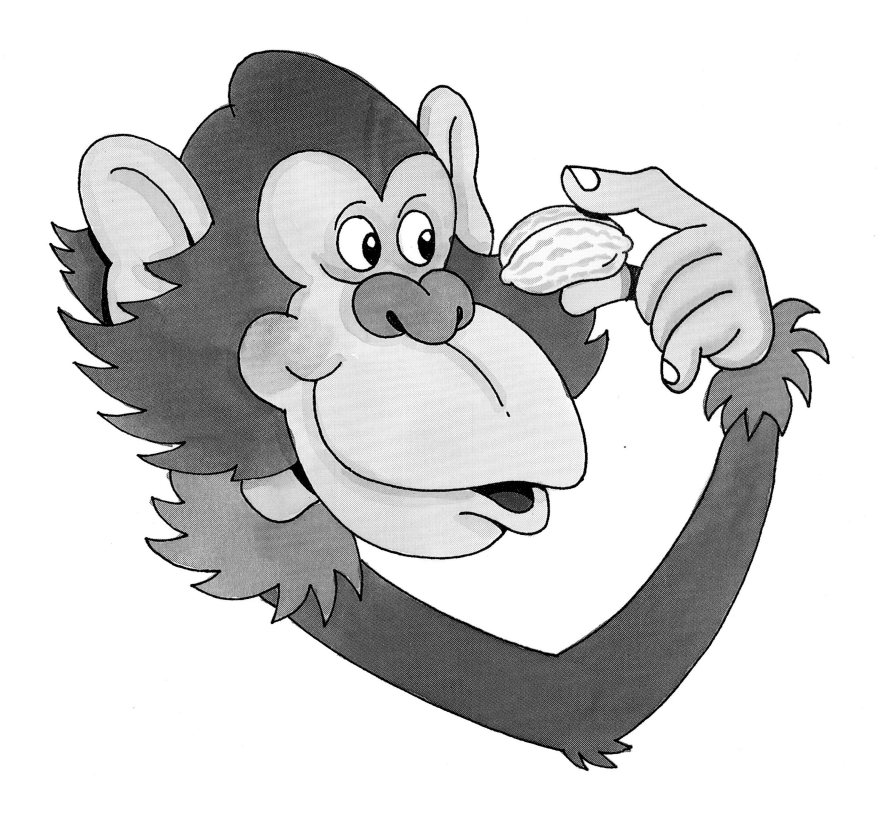

Here is a **n**ut.

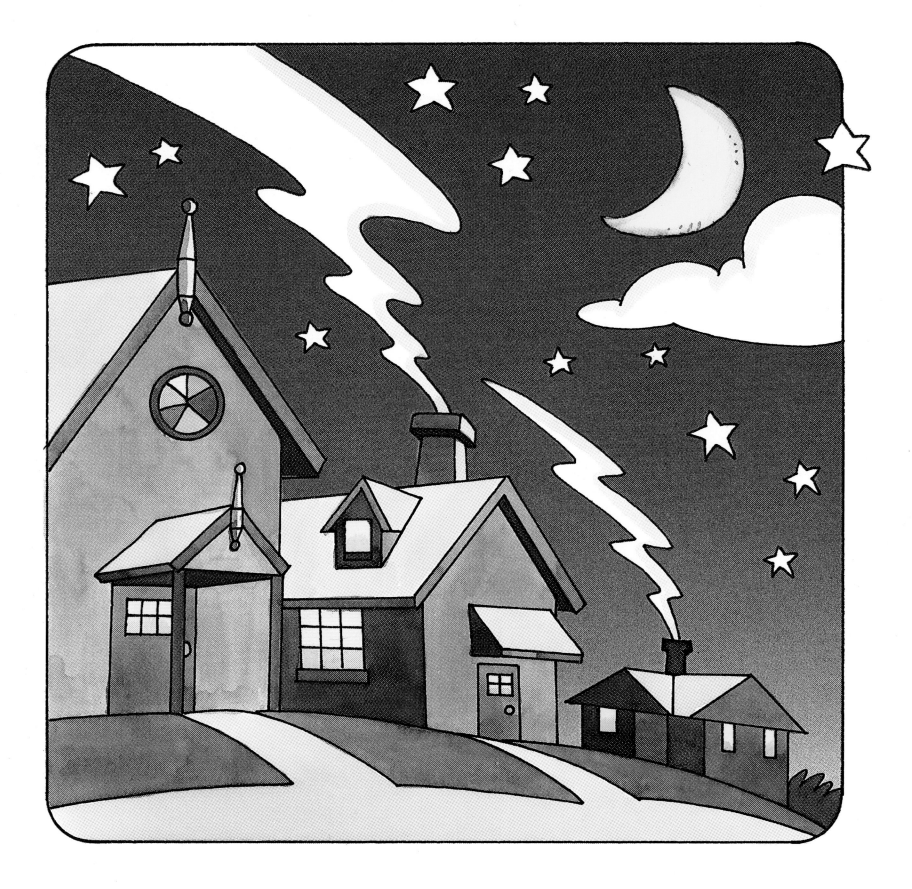

Here is the **n**ight.

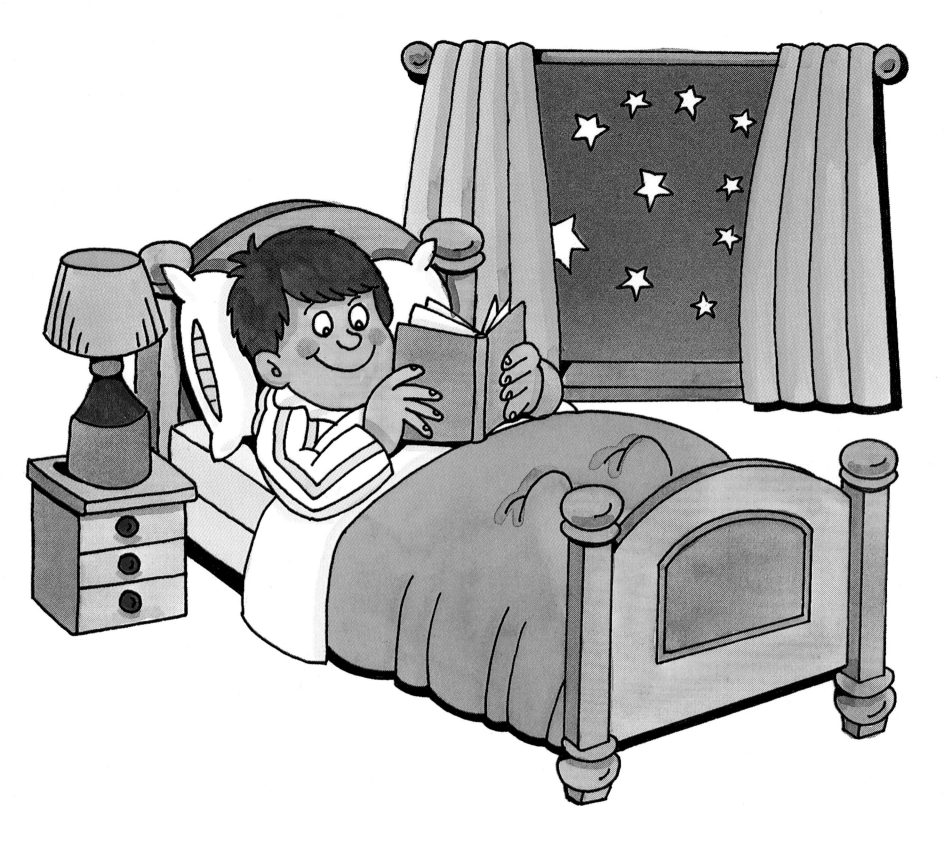

Time for bed.
" Good night!"

I love noodles—
oodles of noodles.
I love noodles
with lots of sauce!

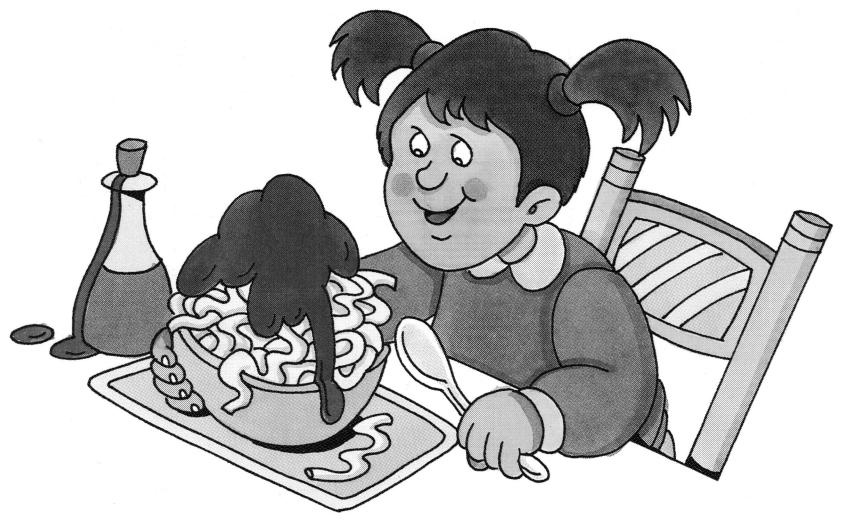